Selections from the Production

MY FAIR LADY

MUSIC BY
FREDERICK LOEWE

BOOK AND LYRICS BY
ALAN JAY LERNER

Easy-to-Play Piano Arrangements

by **WILLIAM STICKLES**

Contents

CHAPPELL & CO. INC.
609 FIFTH AVE. NEW YORK 17, N.Y.

I COULD HAVE DANCED ALL NIGHT

Words by
ALAN JAY LERNER

Music by
FREDERICK LOEWE

9315-15

so _____ ex - cit - ing, _____

Why all at once _____

my heart took flight. _____

I on - ly know _____

when {she}{he} be - gan to dance ____ with me, ____ I could have danced, danced, danced, ____ all night.

p I could have all night. ____

ON THE STREET WHERE YOU LIVE

Words by
ALAN JAY LERNER

Words by
FREDERICK LOEWE

9315-15

live._____ And _mf_ oh,_____ the tow - er - ing

feel - ing,_____ Just to know_____ some - how you are

near! _____ The o - ver pow - er - ing feel - ing_____

That an - y se - cond you may sud - den - ly ap - pear! _____

9315- 15

Peo - ple stop and stare, they don't both - er me; For there's

no-where else on earth that I would rath - er be. Let the time go by,

I won't care if I can be here on the

street where you live. I have live.

GET ME TO CHURCH ON TIME

Words by
ALAN JAY LERNER

Music by
FREDERICK LOEWE

9315-15

I'VE GROWN ACCUSTOMED TO HER FACE

Words by
ALAN JAY LERNER

Music by
FREDERICK LOEWE

9315-15

na - ture to me now; _____ Like breath - ing out and breath - ing in. _____

I was se - rene - ly in - de - pen - dent and con - tent be - fore we met;

Sure - ly I could al - ways be that way a - gain and yet, I've grown ac - cus - tomed to her looks; Ac -

cus - tomed to her voice; Ac - cus - tomed to her face. _____ I've grown ac -

cus-tomed to her face, _____ She al-most makes the day be-gin. _____

I'm ver-y grate-ful she's a wo-man and so eas-y to for-get;

Rath-er like a hab-it one can al-ways break and yet, I've grown ac-cus-tomed to the trace of

some-thing in the air; Ac- cus-tomed to her face. _____